The Absence of a Mother's Love

Marquis Dorsey

Table of Contents

Dedication

I am the voice of the crack babies and the ears of the parents that uses and I want to bridge the gap.

Acknowledgements

I will like to acknowledge all the children that have no voice and just want to feel loved because it's important for everyone to experience love at least one time before they die especially because our young people dying before they can even make their parents proud.

Prologue

A conversation between a boy and his mother

"Mom, why don't you love me?" the son asked, tears streaming down his face, in desperate need of an answer.

His mother looked at him, her eyes glazed over and her body swaying slightly. She was high, and her alter ego, "Shell," had taken over.

"It's funny you ask that, and to be frank, I don't have a clear-cut answer for you," she replied, her voice slurred. "I want to love you, I just don't know how. The love that I want to displace, I can't because Shell has a hold on me."

The son looked at his mother with confusion and sadness. He had heard this before, and it hurt him deeply every time. He couldn't understand why his own mother couldn't love him.

"But mom, why can't you overcome Shell?" he asked, desperation in his voice.

"See, baby, Shell isn't something you can just overcome," she said, her voice trailing off. "Especially when I have no other outlet and wasn't taught how to effectively deal with my own demons. See, Shell owns me because she makes me feel good and forget everything that ever hurt me, and she makes me forget that I'm not a good mother."

"Mom, you are a great mother," the son said, tears still streaming down his face.

"No, no, no, you want the truth, so I'll give you the truth," the mother said, her voice rising. "The reason why I can't love you is that I'm ashamed of who I see when I look in the mirror."

"Mom, you are beautiful," the son said, trying to comfort her.

"Baby, stop talking, and let me get through this," she said, cutting him off. "You want to know why Shell exists, and I put her over my own children, whom I carried for nine months is, because of the way I wasn't loved."

The son looked at his mother, trying to understand what she was saying. He had heard bits and pieces of her story before, but he had never heard her say it all at once.

"You want me to tell you?" she asked, her voice shaking.

"Mom, it seems like you are getting emotional. Let's stop. I hate seeing you cry; I don't want you to relive moments that made shell be born."

"It's time for me to finally get it off my chest and release shell." "But mom.... "

"Boy, if you interrupt me one more time!!!"

"I'm sorry, Mom."

"From the first day I was born, my mom didn't love me enough to even keep me, and when I was with her, I didn't feel good enough to be her child."

The son felt a pang of sympathy for his mother.

He had heard that his grandmother had abandoned his mother when she was a baby, but he had never really thought about how it must have affected her.

"The reason I moved away from my siblings is that they all looked down on me and made me feel like the black sheep of the family," the mother continued. "I used to seek validation from people who didn't give two fucks about me unless I was of some use to them."

The son felt a deep sadness for his mother. He knew how it felt to seek validation from others and

5

not get it. He wondered if his mother had ever felt validated by him.

"It was no mental health outlets when I was younger," the mother said. "We all turned to drugs when we needed to vent because if we expressed ourselves, we were just labeled as crazy. Even worse, as a woman, we were labeled crazy and outlandish. But since you want to know why I turned to Shell as an outlet because what else was I supposed to do when I didn't have a mother's love and had my first child at 16 and another at 17, and I'm in and out of shelters."

"Mo-"

"Boy, shut up!"

His mother took a deep breath before she continued. "Let's take it a step further. How about being a child who my mom didn't fight to keep and growing up in Foster care and being beaten and raped on a daily basis? How about being beaten because I'm left-handed, and they deemed me to be intellectually unstable just because I was fucking left-handed!!!!!"

The son listened to his mother's words, feeling a mix of sadness and anger. "I'm sorry, son. I didn't mean to yell at you. It's just that it's so hard for me to talk about this. But I need to get it off my chest.

You see, I've been carrying this burden for too long, and it's time for me to release it. You deserve to know the truth. I turned to drugs because I was trying to escape the pain. It was the only way I knew how to cope. And now, I'm stuck in this vicious cycle. Try to stop, but I always end up going back."

The son listened intently as his mother spoke, tears streaming down her face as she recounted the horrors of her past. It was difficult to hear but he knew it was important for her to finally open up and let it all out.

"I'm so sorry, Mom," he said, his voice choked with emotion. "I had no idea."

"It's not your fault, baby," my mother said softly, reaching out to wipe away his tears. "It's not your fault at all."

He took a deep breath and tried to compose himself, wanting to be strong for his mother. "So what happened next?" he asked her.

"Well, I eventually got out of Foster care and started trying to make a life for myself," his mother said, her voice growing stronger. "But it was hard, you know? I was so damaged from everything that had happened to me, and I didn't know how to deal with it. So I turned to drugs."

"But why, Mom?" he asked. "Why didn't you try to get help?"

"Because I didn't know how," his mother said with a shrug. "I didn't have anyone to turn to, no one who could understand what I had been through. And when I got high, it was like all the pain and hurt just disappeared for a little while."

"But what about us, Mom?" he said, his voice rising in frustration. "What about your kids?"

His mother hung her head, and he could see the shame and guilt in her eyes. "I know, baby," she said softly. "I know I wasn't the mother you deserved. But I tried, you know? I really did. I tried to make sure you all had a roof over your heads and food in your bellies. I just couldn't be the mother you needed me to be all the time."

He nodded slowly, feeling a mix of anger and sadness. It was hard to hear his mother admit to all of this, but at the same time, it felt like a weight was being lifted off of her.

"What can we do to help you, Mom?" he asked her.

"How can we support you?"

His mother sighed heavily. "I don't know, baby," she said. "I wish I did. I'm still struggling with my addiction, and I know I need to get clean. But it's so hard, you know? Sometimes I feel like it's the only thing keeping me going."

"I don't know why I couldn't love you to your standards, but I know I wouldn't have let half of the things happen to me happen to any of y'all," replied the mother. "I would have killed and died for y'all just to be safe, but the drugs had this fucking hold on me."

The son looked at her with a mix of concern and understanding.

"So you know what I did for my kids even while I was addicted to drugs?" continued the mother.

"What, mom?"

"I played crazy enough to have some type of resource coming in from the government, a house from Section 8, and some food stamps. To make sure you all had something. I had a 7th-grade graduation and didn't even know how to help you all with your homework," explained the mother.

The son listened attentively, taking in every word.

"I loved you based on how I was taught to love. I can still see the big white hairy man coming into my room in Foster care to have his way with me, and nobody there to love me enough to even tell him to stop," said the mother, her voice shaking with emotion. "I can still smell how sweaty the horrible smell of beer on his breath every night. Nobody even helped me once until my mom finally came to get us after she got her things together. At that point, I hated my life and didn't want to live."

"I knew when I got older and stronger, nobody would ever be able to serve my mom any drugs again," continued the mother, her voice becoming more determined. "Now, don't get me wrong, I had two brothers on the same mission. One went to prison for 15 years, and the other one just had to get away to keep his sanity; however, he always made sure he stopped by to make sure we was good, and if he heard anybody sold her drugs, they both handled it."

He couldn't help but feel a sense of obligation to protect his mother, no matter the cost. He couldn't wait for it to be his turn to protect her; even if it meant going to jail for the rest of his life, he would do it to keep her safe. All he ever wanted was to make sure she was safe, to shield her from the pain and suffering that life had dealt her. He wondered why she never told him about the things she went through, why she kept it all inside.

"Mom, I didn't know why you didn't tell me," he said aloud.

"Tell you for what so that you can do what exactly? Hurt with me?" His mother responded.

"See, that's real love when I go through everything I went through, and I shield you all from it and just take the scrutiny from you and everybody else, and I still manage to just take it. I take all the knives to the back and I still stand tall and you say I don't love you. How dare you when I gave you everything I never had, even when I split you all up. Instead of foster care, you all went to different people in the family.

"Mom, I get it; you loved us enough to get us through life, and that was enough."

"Son, words cannot express the sorrow I feel for everything you've experienced. I failed you. I know I did. But I was not in control of myself. Was but an infant leaching onto its mother's nipple for every ounce of nutrients. I was breastfed the poison that essentially became my God. If you didn't know who I was, it's because I didn't either. I wish I had the strength to have fought harder for you. Then maybe, just maybe, I could've protected you from me, from

11

the wickedness of this world! My sins have cost you more than the checks I could cash. The abuse, verbal, physical, and sexual, are all a thorn to the crown of my head and a piercing to my heart."

"Son, I'm hurting because you hurt. With every burden you've carried, you've persevered, and I'm proud of you. Everything meant to break you only made you stronger, and that is no thanks to me. I understand why you have lived in a cocoon most of your life. You, too, could have spiraled down the same dark pathway as I....but for whatever reason, you did not."

Chapter 1:
How It Started

As a child that grew up accustomed to abuse, my life was never easy. Growing up with a mother addicted to drugs certainly didn't help. When I finally confronted my mother about everything she had put me through, I expected her to fight back and justify her actions. But instead, she looked at me with sorrow in her eyes and took responsibility for what had happened. I was taken aback. She told me about her own struggles, how she had been trapped in a cycle of addiction and abuse since she was a child, and how she had never had the strength to fight back.

As she spoke, I could see the deep wounds that had been inflicted upon her soul. For the first time, I realized that she was just as much a victim as I was. Despite everything that happened, I knew that my mother did what she had to do to get us through life. But even as she spoke, she was still trying to protect me.

I wanted to scream at her, to tell her that all I had ever wanted was for her to be there for me, to love me unconditionally. But as I looked into her eyes, I could see the truth of her words. She had done everything she could to protect us, to shield us from the horrors of her own life. And even though she had failed in so many ways, she had also given us the strength and resilience to survive.

The abuse I suffered, both physical and emotional, left a permanent mark on me. I couldn't forget the pain and hurt that I had endured. It was like a thorn to the crown of my head and a piercing to my heart. Despite all of this, I couldn't help but feel a sense of betrayal from my mother. I knew that she loved me in her own way, but I also wished that she had fought harder for me.

But as I looked at my mother, I could see the pain in her eyes. She had done the best she could with the cards she had been dealt. I knew that she had failed me, but I also knew that she was fighting her own battles. And in that moment, I realized that I had to let go of the anger and resentment that I had been holding onto for so long. My mother was not perfect, but she had done everything she could to protect me and my siblings. And for that, I was grateful.

Chapter 2:
The Battle Between Mom And Shell

Mom, it's okay to leave shell alone because we need you more. "Mom, it's okay to leave shell alone,"

Shut up, shell said in a mocking tone. Your mother will forever be in my debt because when nobody else made her forget her past, I did. When nobody else made her feel worthy, I did, so who do you think she will choose, me or "her kids," the mockery continues. Mom, I cried out as she was high and couldn't respond. Shell replied boy leave me alone and go play. I just wanted you to know I love you I said as tears fail down my face. Shell replied yeah yeah, I love you too.

Now this is the battle I have seen my mother have and, most time, lost to drugs. When she wasn't on drugs, she was the best mother ever, but whenever she was under the influence of drugs, my siblings called her shell. I hated shell so much, but I had to love her because, in reality, she was my mom, but I realized early in life that my mom was battling a battle no one understood but her and God, so I had to grow a level of sympathy for her even if she didn't have it for us because even though she didn't teach us much, she taught us how to survive..... Or she taught us wrong....

She taught my sister how to use men for things that they wanted and taught them to use their bodies to make a man fold to their natural beauty. She taught my brothers and me how to protect ourselves from danger and how to take everything we wanted, even if it didn't belong to us. Shell will tell my sister things like don't let no man just give you a wet ass, and you ain't get nothing from it. That was just her way of survival. If you ask me, I think my mom was molested and raped as a child made her destroy the nature of intimacy with a special two people, and she just found pleasure in allowing men to just want nothing from her but her body. So she used to tell us stories about a man who had to bring something to the table if she was ever going to lie down with him, no matter how he looked. That was the best way she knew how to take the power of sex back from her being raped daily by that big hairy man in foster care. I wish I could have protected my mom from him. I have so much anger built up inside of me for him hurting my mom and I don't want to control it. She would let people know how nicely built she was as a young adult and how she controlled men. Now I know it was payback from the one man she couldn't control. You only hear about the negative sides of people who use drugs, but you never hear

16

why they use drugs and I'm glad I listened to why because now, as an adult, I hear my mom's side very clearly, and nobody can tell me she isn't the best mom in the world. I honestly only had this horrible depiction of who you were because all my life, people told me about shell, and I never got to know my mom for myself. It's not your fault that you went through everything that you went through, but it's your fault that you never defended yourself. You are so used to people talking down on you that you never speak up for yourself. Mom, I love you enough for both of us. I remember our walks to save a lot so that you could get us some food so that we wouldn't go hungry and you being up and age and having to stop every other block from taking a break but you did it for us and that's a way you showed your love. Or when you couldn't buy us Christmas gifts, you made sure we had goodfella boxes just so we could have something to open on Christmas Day. That's how you showed your love. It's time for you to stop being afraid of your past and start addressing these mutha fuckas. You have a bunch of sons that will die and kill for you, so don't take shit from anybody else. Mom, please put shell away. We know your childhood is what made you create shell because you had to protect yourself from the cruel cold streets but you don't have to be that anymore. How can I get mad at you for only knowing one way to love and battling between being a great mother and making sure you never get hurt again? Mom, shell can't control you anymore. You have all the power. You just have to believe and be the strong person we know you to be. Can't nobody stop you, not even your mom. It's time for you to be the best we know you to be. They see a crackhead; I see a broken mother trying to keep fighting to give her children the little life she has left in there. You didn't deserve a man breaking into your house while your daughter was there to jump on you and beat you almost to death while your daughter watched. It's not your fault. Stop blaming yourself.

Chapter 3:
Nobody Should Live Like This

God, why me? Why do I have to be the one born into a family that's not rich? Full of convicted felons and a mother that abuses drugs? Wasn't I worthy enough to come from a rich and well-off family with a history of degrees and business ideas? No, I have to be in the house where the lights get turned off, and my 12-year-old brother Quan has to sell drugs and rob to get them turned back on. I have to be in the house where food is limited, where the water gets turned off, and we have to fill the tub up with water from the neighbor's water holes just to be able to flush the toilet. Or having to ask for food or steal it just to eat. Trying to figure out what my identity is. If I wanted to be an athlete or a guy that ran the streets and sold drugs because that was the best thing to do in my neighborhood because the dope boys were the neighborhood hero. Nooooo, I can't do that. I promised I'd never sell drugs because I saw how it broke my household up and made my mom somebody I never saw before. I swore never to make another child endure what I had to go through as a child. Then dark days, not everybody can make it out or see the light of success. It's not fair for a child to ever have to suffer or grow up before their time.

Why couldn't my brother have a childhood? Because he was too busy being the man of the house and buying us uniforms at 12 and 13 years old. How can I not respect and honor him when he gave me the opportunity to be a kid, and he put himself last? Why couldn't our lives be better? But think about it, Quis, you had to go through everything you went through so that you could be that for somebody else that wasn't as strong as you. How many children are you helping in your career that you can relate to that are going through what you're going through? Man, fuck that. I still feel like no child should go through that, watching friends die and go to jail right in front of you, or seeing your mom being served, or even overdosing happening in your face and it's just you in the house. Or how about this, this is a good one, how about being 10 and getting head so good from a lady your mom had living with you even though you felt violated, you couldn't ask for help because if you did as a boy or man you would be shamed. And now you have to deal with the fact that you weren't ready for this level of sexual exclusivity but it's forced on you so you have to just take it. That's not the craziest part in this. The part that makes it wild is you start to like it and kind of put it in your mind that you're a couple, and at 10 years old, you have to break it off with a grown woman who refuses to stop, not

20

because she loves you but because she has more power than you.

I didn't have the strength to tell my mom when this happened. Because I was scared and confused. What did I know? I was just a child. While I did realize it was wrong and tried to put an end to it, I didn't really understand then what was happening. My mom found out later about it and it took a toll on her. She was high when she figured it out and as you can imagine, she did not take it well.

Why didn't you tell me? Shell yelled at me from across the room. I'm sorry, mom. I didn't understand. I was scared.

You should have told me!

Then she beat me hard until I cried. My brother Quan stepped in and tried to make light of the situation. He was young too and I guess, even he did not understand the severity of the situation.

Later on, mom came to me and hugged me close to her chest. Tears were falling down her cheeks as she sobbed.

I'm sorry, baby. I should have protected you. I'm so sorry.

I told mom that it wasn't her fault but I knew she blamed herself and felt as if she'd failed me. She'd been molested herself in her childhood and felt that she couldn't save me from the path that befell her.

Later, Quan jokingly asked me if I really got my dick sucked and when I said yes, he tried to high five me. He said that it was cool that I was sexually active. I know that sounds weird but this is how most men reacted when they heard the news. I was hailed a hero and championed instead of protected and supported. It really says something about the state of our society and how people treat issues related to the mental health of men.

Now this is where it gets even more fucked up. You listening? Yeah, I'm still here. Okay, so most guys start having girlfriends and really start having sex about 13 or 14 in our community. So now, when I'm ready to have a girlfriend, I am stuck in a relationship that will never blossom because of the experience that 1 have from a grown experienced woman. Because a 13-year-old girl doesn't know how to do the tricks she knows how to do, so I'm constantly replacing women all my life or cheating on them because I haven't found the one girl that compared to her as a child. This is an even better one. How about me not even really giving women a fair chance to love me because in my mind my mom doesn't love me and never has so I already suffered the first heartbreak that most 13-year-old boys suffer with a romantic partner. When I couldn't perform she tied my testicles and penis off so that I could get hard for her and when I couldn't get hard for she made me feel bad and used to say things like. I never was enough for any man, so I knew you wouldn't want me either. Why am I not enough I should just end my life because no man wants me.

This is when I would start feeling horrible for her and have to think about pornos books of attractive women I used to watch on the Playboy books my brother hid under his mattress so that I wasn't like the other men that didn't want her and she wouldn't "end her life" I always put her before me because I always wanted to help people even though I was hurting the most. What makes it worse is I still felt cool to be a young boy getting vagina. It didn't matter who it came from at that time. Well, at least that's what my community told me.

Sexual abuse really fucks you up. Even more so if you experience it as a child. It's been years but I can still remember the first time it happened as if it were yesterday. I was just a child, innocent and naive, and had no idea what was happening to me. It left me feeling confused, violated, and alone.

As I grew older, the memories of the abuse became more vivid. I couldn't escape them, and they haunted me at every turn. I became angry and bitter, pushing away anyone who tried to get close to me. I began to see women as objects, using them for my own pleasure and discarding them when I was done. I didn't care about their feelings or emotions; all I wanted was to satisfy my own desires.

I feel like my mom carried me for 9 months, gave me up on day one, and since she came back to get me, I've been fighting for my life in every sense. So in my mind, if she carried me for 9 months and I never felt love, I knew a woman who didn't know me would never love me, and I moved accordingly. I never cared if a girl cheated on me because I expected them to do that already, so when they did, our relationship dynamic didn't change because I trust a snake to bite me. I just dogged them even harder and knew in my mind I would never marry them.

Sex became meaningless to me. It was no longer an act of intimacy or love, but rather a way to numb the pain and escape the memories of the past. I would go from one sexual encounter to another, hoping that the next one would make me feel something, anything. But it never did. I was left feeling empty and hollow, with a deep sense of shame and self-loathing.

I tried to ignore the impact that the abuse had on me, but it was always there, lurking in the background. It affected every aspect of my life, from my relationships to my work. I had trouble trusting people, and I always felt like I was keeping a part of myself hidden from the world.

It wasn't until I sought help from a therapist that I began to understand the full extent of the damage that the abuse had caused. I had to confront the pain and trauma head-on, which was terrifying at first. But as I worked through my issues, I began to see a glimmer of hope. I realized that I didn't have to live my life as a victim, and that I could take control of my own healing.

It's been a long and difficult journey, but I am now in a much better place. I've learned to see women as individuals with their own thoughts and feelings, rather than objects to be used for my own pleasure. I've discovered that sex can be a beautiful and meaningful act, one that can bring people together and create a deep sense of intimacy and connection.

Of course, I still have moments of fear and insecurity. The scars of my past will always be a part of me. But I no longer let them control my life. I've learned to be kinder to myself, and to forgive myself for the mistakes I've made. I'm no longer running from my past, but rather embracing it as a part of who I am.

I know that there are many others out there who have experienced sexual abuse, and I want them to know that there is hope. Healing is possible, but it takes time and effort. It's not an easy road, but it's a journey that's worth taking.

In all honesty, sexual abuse is a traumatic experience that can have a profound impact on a person's life. It can lead to feelings of shame, guilt, and self-loathing, as well as a distorted view of sex and relationships. However, with the right support and guidance, it's possible to heal and move forward. It's a difficult journey, but one that's worth taking for the sake of your own well-being and happiness.

I spent most of my life chasing after meaningless relationships, never really finding any true emotional connection with anyone. But then I met Tyesha, and everything changed.

From the moment I laid eyes on her, I knew she was different. There was something about her that drew me in, something that made me want to get to know her better. And as we got to know each other, I found myself falling in love with her in a way I never thought possible.

Tyesha is beautiful, of course, with her gorgeous hair and her warm brown eyes that always seem to sparkle with laughter. But it's not just her physical appearance that draws me to her. It's her personality, her kindness, and her intelligence.

She's one of the most thoughtful people I've ever met, always going out of her way to do something nice for someone else. Whether it's baking cookies for a friend who's feeling down or sending a thoughtful text to check in on someone who's been going through a tough time, Tyesha is always there for the people she cares about.

And she's so intelligent, too. I love having conversations with her, because she always has something interesting and insightful to say. She's incredibly well-read, and she's always learning something new. I love how passionate she is about the things she cares about, whether it's politics or art or social justice.

But most of all, I love the way Tyesha makes me feel. When I'm with her, I feel like I'm home. She's the first person I want to tell my good news to, and the first person I turn to when I'm feeling down. I love the way she makes me laugh, and the way she always knows just what to say to make me feel better.

I never thought I'd find someone who would make me want to give up my old ways of casual dating and settle down. But with Tyesha, it feels like the most natural thing in the world. I want to build a life with her, to grow old together and experience all of life's ups and downs side by side.

Sometimes I still can't believe how lucky I am to have her in my life. I used to think that true love was just a fairy tale, something that only happened in movies or books. But with Tyesha, it feels like anything is possible. She's my soulmate, my partner, my best friend. I can't imagine my life without her.

In the past, I was content to float through life, never really attaching myself to anyone or anything. But with Tyesha, I feel like I have a purpose. I want to be the best partner I can be for her, to support her in everything she does, and to love her with all of my heart. She's changed me in ways I never thought possible, and I am forever grateful for her presence in my life.

I believe Tyesha is the love of my life. She's beautiful, intelligent, and kind, but most of all, she makes me feel like I've finally found my place in the world. I can't wait to spend the rest of my life with her, building a future together filled with love, laughter, and all the little moments that make life worth living.

As I reflect on my past and how my mom raised us, I can't help but think about how Tyesha fits into the picture. With her by my side, I feel like I'm ready for anything life throws at me. Together, we'll face whatever challenges come our way and build a future filled with love and strength. Tyesha has given me a sense of purpose, and with her, I feel like I've finally found my place in the world.

My mom was a lot of things, but stupid wasn't one of them. She didn't give me much school wisdom, but she had the streets on lock. She was really the real thug, street guy, animal, warrior in the family. It's not a coincidence that all of her children survived even in her absence. As a child, we were essentially built for moments like this. Like she knew the situation she put us in and prepared us for them.

The children that you bump into that aren't as built as you are to weather the storm like you were now have a blueprint to follow. You give children hope and aspirations to keep fighting because they didn't have hope until some of them met you. Now they have the ability to see into the future and have a role model that's from the backgrounds they are from, and they are now inspired to be exactly or, if not better than, what you are today.

Chapter 4:
Brotherly Love

I won't apologize. Apologize for what? For how I raised you? I was only able to teach you the way I was taught. You used to be on trash, and we both laughed while I was visiting him in prison. However, I will apologize for the mental turmoil you had to endure because of those teachings. You are breaking it down like I only went through it mentally. Don't be condescending. If you are going to apologize, apologize for everything, like the emotional and physical abuse I had to endure. Your teachings on how to fight were fucked up. Every day, you used to lock me in the basement and punch me until I had a headache. What if I didn't want to learn how to fight? What if I wanted to be a regular kid that played sports? Why were you trying to prepare me for the world like you had to if you had me? You were raising me bipolar. You didn't know if you wanted me to be prepared for the streets or go to college. That was a hard time trying to identify who I was as a kid.

You have to understand it from my perspective. How could I give you something that I didn't have myself? Bro, fuck your perspective. You used that as an excuse to build the person you wanted to be in my eyes, like everything you wanted to do good, you made me do. You only went to college just so you could show me that it's possible, but what if I didn't want to go? It's like you made me live the dream you always wanted to live. Nigga, you were in college; I'm not sure why you couldn't finish that shit. I hated school. But school came so naturally to you. You always were giftedly smart, so I just wanted to push you to your potential. You weren't going to be another waste of talent in the streets, talking about has been stories. Yeah, you pushed me to college, but you weren't even there to help me get through college. Damn, nigga, you could have been there at least, since you were making me live the dream you wanted me to live. I just don't understand your train of thought.

If you would just listen, I can explain! That's been the nature of our entire relationship since we were kids. I shut up and followed orders, and you barked them out. You act like I didn't feel the same thing. You were going through it; there was only so much you could shield me from in a 3-bedroom, one-bathroom house. Listen to what? How you tried to be a good big brother, but you clearly did a horrible job at that.

STOP CUTTING ME OFF!

"Nigga, you cutting me off!"

"Calm the fuck down and listen!" He shows his dominance to get me to listen. The entire prison visitation room comes to silence.

You have to understand that I was ten years old when Mama told me that I had to be the man of the house. At that time, I didn't fully know what that meant, but I figured it out soon enough. This is when Mama started leaving us in the house for a day by ourselves and spending all her money on dope. So that's when I had to make a choice: either let us starve, or go out and get some money so we can eat. I chose the latter. Do you think it was an easy decision for me to make at ten, where I couldn't get a job to take on the responsibilities of being the man of the house? Why couldn't I have a childhood? Where were my outlets? You played little league football. I didn't play football until my 11th grade year.

I put all my dreams to the side to make sure the family was good, and you're talking to me like I left you stranded, nigga. I took you as far as I could as a 10-year-old father. I didn't know you were going through that, bro, because I kept everything away from you and let you live your childhood, unlike I had. Even though selling weed and crack is how I made the most of my money, I started out breaking into garages. Then I graduated to breaking into houses. The money that I made from that kept us fed, but it wasn't consistent, which is why the dope game became my main focus. As time went on, Mama's addiction became more obvious.

You think it wasn't obvious for me, bro? Just because I'm the baby in the family doesn't mean I wasn't going through what y'all went through. See, there you go cutting me off again. My bad. Our struggle became center stage for the rest of the neighborhood to see. That was tough! I think that was when I started to get worse. I honestly didn't give a fuck whether I lived or died. This was my pre-teen years, from the age of ten to thirteen. DAMN!!!!

How can you always preach to always love Mama, but she never loved us? "No matter what, baby bro, that's still our mama, and you should always honor and respect her." If you say so.

I had to sacrifice my entire childhood to make sure that there was food on the table, clothes on our backs, and that y'all were protected. I HATED THAT SHIT! I remember times when I would just snap out because I was fed up with having to be "the man of the house." I'm not saying that Mama didn't do her part to make sure we kept a roof over our heads, food in the fridge at times, and bought us school clothes every blue moon because she did.

However, I was the one TAKING PENITENTIARY CHANCES AS A LITTLE BOY JUST SO WE COULD HAVE THE SHIT THAT WE NEEDED CONSISTENTLY!!!!

Wait! I need to say this... When I was fourteen, I caught Mama smoking crack in the bathroom. "I was nine; I went through it with you!!!!" I yelled. I smacked the pipe out of her hand, and she was so mad that she beat me like I wasn't even her son. That night was the first time that I dropped a nigga, which was another turning point for me in my life, but it was only for the worse. I had no more regard for human life, but I still maintained my ability to think, so I wasn't overly reckless. I swear I've cried myself to sleep a few times growing up because of all the stress and mental anguish that I was going through at that time, but I hid it from the family and my niggas in the streets.

Chapter 5:
Saint or Villain? How About Both?

As I looked around at my surroundings, I couldn't help but feel like I was trapped in a nightmare. Our house was falling apart, with holes in the roof and mold growing on the walls. The smell of drugs and cigarette smoke permeated the air.

Growing up in poverty was not easy. My mother's drug addiction made it even harder. I often felt like I had to be the parent, taking care of myself, my mom and my siblings.

But it wasn't just the physical conditions of our home that made life difficult. It was the constant stress and anxiety of wondering where our next meal would come from, or if we would be able to pay the rent on time.

And as I got older, I began to realize just how much my upbringing had affected my sense of self. I struggled to figure out who I was and where I fit in the world.

I envied those who came from wealthy families, who never had to worry about basic necessities like food and shelter. I longed to be able to pursue my dreams without the burden of financial insecurity holding me back.

But despite all of the challenges we faced, I knew that my family was still full of love. My mother may have had her demons, but she also had a heart of gold. She taught us how to be compassionate and resilient, even in the face of adversity.

And I knew that I would never take my experiences for granted. They had shaped me into the person I was today, and I was determined to use my struggles to help others who were going through similar situations.

Even though it was hard, I found a sense of purpose in my struggles. I knew that I was strong enough to overcome any obstacle that came my way, and that I had the power to make a difference in the world.

So even though I had moments of despair and frustration, I never lost hope. I knew that with hard work and determination, I could create a better life for myself and my family. And that was what kept me going, even on the darkest of days.

I remember the days when my mom was the shining star of our family. Her smile was infectious, and her warmth could light up any room. But those days were few and far between. Her addiction to drugs had a grip on her that was hard to shake off, and it changed her in ways that I could never have imagined.

It was a constant struggle to keep our family afloat. There were days when we didn't have enough food to eat, and we would all go to bed hungry. But even on those days, my mom would still try to feed anybody that came to our door. She would make sure that they had a warm meal and a place to stay for the night. She had a heart of gold, and nothing could ever change that.

But when she was under the influence, she was a completely different person. It was hard to watch my mom spiral out of control. She would disappear into herself for days on end, leaving us to fend for ourselves. I would worry about her constantly, wondering if she was safe or if she would ever come back. But every time she did, she would be high and distant, as if she was a completely different person.

It was during those moments that I felt the most alone. My mom was always there for us when she was sober, but when she was high, it was like she didn't even know who we were. It was a painful experience that left me feeling helpless and lost.

Despite all of this, my mom taught us how to survive in this harsh reality. She showed us how to be resilient and how to never give up. She instilled in us the value of hard work and the importance of looking out for each other. These were lessons that I would carry with me for the rest of my life.

As I grew older, I began to understand the full extent of my mom's addiction. It was a disease that had taken over her life, and it was something that she couldn't control. It was heartbreaking to see her suffer, but it was also a reminder that we needed to be there for her, even when she couldn't be there for us.

There were moments of hope, when my mom would try to get clean and start over. But they were always short-lived. Her addiction was too strong, and it would pull her back in every time. It was a vicious cycle that we couldn't break, no matter how hard we tried.

In the end, my mom's addiction took her life. It was a devastating loss that I still feel to this day. But even in death, she taught me something valuable. She taught me that addiction is a real and dangerous disease, one that can destroy lives and tear families apart. She taught me that we need to be there for each other, no matter what.

My mom was the most compassionate person I had ever known, and even in her darkest moments, she still tried to show love and kindness to those around her. She may have been taken too soon, but her memory lives on in the lessons she taught us and the love she shared with the world.

I remember a specific experience that showcased my mother's beautiful heart. It was a cold winter evening, and our family was struggling to make ends meet. We had very little food left, and we were worried about how we would manage to make it through the next few days.

As we were sitting down for dinner, there was a knock on the door. It was our neighbor, Mrs. Jenkins. She was an elderly woman who lived alone and had been struggling with her health. She looked frail and tired, and I could see that she was shivering from the cold.

My mother didn't hesitate for a moment. She invited Mrs. Jenkins inside and asked her to sit by the fire. She quickly went to the kitchen and started preparing a meal for her. I could hear her rummaging through the cupboards, trying to find something to serve.

I knew that we didn't have much, but my mother had a way of making even the smallest of meals seem like a feast. She pulled out some bread and cheese, and then she added a few slices of leftover ham that we had from a previous meal. She made a pot of hot tea and poured Mrs. Jenkins a cup.

As we sat around the table, my mother talked to Mrs. Jenkins, asking her about her health and how she was doing. She listened to her stories and shared some of her own. They laughed and joked, and for a moment, it seemed like everything was okay.

I could see the gratitude in Mrs. Jenkins' eyes. She was touched by my mother's kindness, and I could tell that it meant the world to her. She ate her meal slowly, savoring every bite, and my mother kept refilling her cup of tea.

After dinner, my mother packed a few leftovers for Mrs. Jenkins to take home. She also gave her a few extra blankets to keep her warm during the night. Mrs. Jenkins hugged my mother tightly, tears in her eyes, and thanked her for everything.

As she left, my mother turned to us with a smile on her face. "It feels good to help someone," she said. "Even if we don't have much, we can still make a difference in someone's life."

That experience stuck with me, and I've carried it with me ever since. It was a reminder of the kind of person my mother was, and it taught me the value of compassion and empathy.

Despite all of our struggles, my mother never lost her sense of humanity. She never turned her back on someone in need, no matter how much she had to give. Her heart was bigger than any hardship we faced, and she showed us that love and kindness were more important than material possessions.

In a world that can sometimes feel cold and harsh, my mother was a beacon of light. She showed us that even in the darkest of moments, we can still find a way to spread love and joy. She taught us to look beyond ourselves and to see the needs of those around us.

That winter evening with Mrs. Jenkins was just one example of my mother's beautiful heart. But it was a moment that I will always cherish, and it's a reminder of the kind of person I want to be. I want to carry on my mother's legacy of kindness and compassion, and I want to make a difference in the lives of those around me, just as she did.

As much as I loved my mother and admired her for her kindness and compassion, I also knew that there was another side to her. A side that was dark and scary, and that I couldn't understand. I saw her as two different people, and it was hard for me to reconcile the two.

There was the person my mother was when she was sober. This was the person that I loved and admired. She was kind, loving, and compassionate. She would do anything for anyone, even if it meant sacrificing her own needs. She was always there for us, and she taught us the importance of family and community.

But then there was the person my mother became when she was high. This was the person that I called "shell," because it felt like she was just a shell of herself. She was mean, degrading, and abusive. She would lash out at us for no reason, and her words were like daggers that cut deep.

It was like she was a completely different person. The person I loved and admired was gone, replaced by someone I didn't know. Someone who was scary and unpredictable. Someone I wanted to run away and hide from.

I remember times when my mother would be high, and she would say things to me that I would never forget. Things that would stay with me for years. She would tell me that I was worthless, that I would never amount to anything. She would call me names and make me feel like I was the worst person in the world.

It was hard for me to understand how someone who could be so loving and compassionate could also be so cruel and hurtful. It was like there were two different people living inside of her, and I never knew which one was going to show up.

It was a constant battle for me, trying to reconcile these two different sides of my mother. On one hand, I wanted to love her and be close to her, but on the other hand, I was scared of her and didn't want to be around her when she was high.

It took me a long time to realize that addiction was a disease, and that my mother wasn't in control of her actions when she was high. I learned to separate the person I loved from the addiction that was controlling her.

It wasn't easy, but I knew that my mother was worth fighting for. She had a heart of gold, and I wanted to help her in any way that I could.

She was not perfect, and she still had her moments when she struggled, but she was doing the best she could. And I knew that the person I love was still there, underneath all of the pain and hurt.

Looking back at it now, I realize that my mother will always be two different people to me, but I've learned to love and accept both sides of her. She's not perfect, but she's still my mother, and I'm grateful for the moments of kindness and compassion that she's shown me over the years.

I remember a time in my childhood when I sat in the dimly lit living room, staring at the flickering candle on the coffee table. I couldn't help but feel a sense of despair wash over me. It seemed like every week, the electricity bill was due, and every week, we struggled to come up with the money to pay it.

My mother's drug addiction had taken a toll on our family finances, and we were always behind on bills. But the worst was when the lights would get turned off. It was a constant reminder of just how much we were struggling to make ends meet.

That's when my brother Quan would step in. He was only 12 years old, but he was already street smart and savvy enough to know how to make some quick cash. He would sell drugs and rob people to get the money we needed to turn the lights back on.

I hated that he had to resort to such desperate measures, but I also understood why he did it. We had no other options. My mother was too consumed by her addiction to work, and I was still in school, trying to keep my grades up and make something of myself.

It was a constant cycle of poverty and desperation. We would scrape by for a few weeks, barely making ends meet, and then something would happen - a medical emergency, a car breakdown - and we would be plunged back into darkness, both figuratively and literally.

But even in the midst of all this, we found ways to survive. My mother would cook whatever food we had left in the house and invite our neighbors over to share a meal. We would gather around the candle, telling stories and laughing until our stomachs ached.

It was moments like these that reminded me of the resilience and strength that ran through my family's veins. Despite all of the obstacles we faced, we still found ways to come together and support each other.

But as much as we tried to make the best of our situation, it was impossible to ignore the toll that poverty was taking on our mental health. I struggled with anxiety and depression, always worrying about where our next meal would come from or if we would be able to pay the rent on time.

And my brother, who had been forced to grow up too fast, was struggling with his own demons. He had seen and experienced things that no child should have to, and it was taking a toll on him.

I knew that we needed to find a way out of this cycle of poverty, but it seemed like an impossible task. How could we break free from the chains of addiction and poverty that had been holding us back for so long.

As much as I wanted to believe that things would eventually get better, deep down, I knew that the cycle of poverty and violence would likely continue for my family. Even though my mother tried her best to provide for us, her addiction and mental health issues made it nearly impossible for her to break free from the cycle.

It was a constant battle between hope and despair. There were days when I felt like giving up, when the weight of our struggles felt too heavy to bear. But then there were moments of light, moments when I could see a glimmer of hope on the horizon.

Over the years, I learned to cope with our situation and found solace in improving myself.

Overtime, my mother's addiction worsened, and she eventually lost her battle with drugs. It was a devastating blow, and I felt a mix of emotions - sadness, anger, and even relief that she was no longer suffering.

In the end, I came to the realization that sometimes, no matter how much we want to help, we can't save everyone. The problems my family faced were much larger than any one person could solve. But I could use my experiences to advocate for change and help others who faced similar struggles.

And that's what I set out to do, to try and make a difference in whatever way I could.

Looking back on my childhood, I realize that it was a defining moment in my life. It taught me the value of hard work, resilience, and the importance of community. It also made me appreciate the small things in life and never take anything for granted. While my story may not have a fairy tale ending, it has made me who I am today, and I'm grateful for that.

I knew that I couldn't give up, that I had to keep fighting for a better future for myself and my family. It was a long and difficult road, but I was determined to make it to the other side.

Chapter 6:
Prison Pain From My Brother

Growing up with a drug addict for a mom was not easy for my brother Quan and me. Our childhood was filled with uncertainties, and we had to learn how to survive on our own at a very young age. We had to fend for ourselves, and at times, we had to rely on each other to get by.

Quan was always there for me. He was my father, my brother, and my best friend, all rolled into one. At the age of 10, he took on the role of a father, even though he was just a child himself. I was only 5 at the time, and he had a 5-year age difference over me. He did everything in his power to provide for us, even if it meant doing things that were not always legal.

Quan used to steal, sell drugs, and rob just so that we could have a uniform for school. I remember the times when he would come home with a bag full of clothes that he had stolen from the mall. He would spend hours sorting through the items, trying to find something that would fit us. He always made sure that I had clothes that were my size, and he would wear clothes that were too big for him.

There were times when we didn't have anything to eat, and Quan would go out and steal food from the local grocery store. He was never caught, and he always managed to bring back enough food to last us for a few days. We never knew where he got the food from, and we never asked. We were just happy to have something to eat.

When I got into trouble at school, Quan was always there to bail me out. I remember the times when I would get suspended from school for fighting, and Quan would catch the bus from 8th grade to put me back in school. He would make sure that I got to school on time, and then he would catch the bus back home. He gave up his childhood so that I could have one.

As we got older, our roles started to reverse. I became the one who looked out for Quan. He started to get involved with the wrong crowd, and I knew that I had to do something to stop him. I would talk to him, trying to get him to see that he was heading down the wrong path. At times, he would listen, but most of the time, he would just shrug me off.

One day, I got a call from Quan's friend, telling me that he had been arrested. He had been caught selling drugs, and he was facing a long prison sentence. I was devastated. I knew that I had to do something to help him. I called every lawyer I could find, trying to find someone who could help us. Of course, there's not many people out there willing to help people like us. It was during moments like this that I often believed my mom was right. And that all we had was ourselves.

As I sat across from my brother, I couldn't help but feel a wave of anger wash over me. "Why did you never teach me how to cope with my feelings?" I asked, trying to keep my voice calm.

My brother looked up at me, a pained expression on his face.

"All you did was show me how to fight by locking me in the basement," I said, my voice low.

I swallowed, trying to hold back the tears that threatened to spill over. It was true. My brother had never been one to show his emotions, except when he was punching somebody. I had grown up watching him use violence to deal with his problems, and I had followed in his footsteps, thinking that was the only way to handle things.

"Why is that?" I asked, my voice shaking with emotion. "Do you have anything in life you regret?"

My brother looked down at his hands, and I could see the pain etched on his face. "Honestly, I don't have many regrets," he said, his voice barely above a whisper. "But going to prison and not being present to witness you graduate from high school, college, and getting your master's is the biggest regret of my life."

I felt a lump form in my throat as I listened to him speak. I had never heard him talk about his regrets before, and it was a shock to hear him admit to such a deep-seated pain.

"Having to deal with the stress of being in prison and living with the constant thought of me failing you and the rest of the family is a feeling that I can't explain," my brother continued. "It's a weight that I carry with me every day, and I don't know if I'll ever be able to let it go."

I reached across the table and took my brother's hand in mine. "You didn't fail us," I said, my voice choking with emotion. "You did what you had to do to survive, and we understand that."

My brother looked up at me, tears streaming down his face. "I just wish I could have been there for you," he said. "I wish I could have shown you a better way to cope with your feelings, instead of resorting to violence."

I nodded, understanding the pain that he was feeling. For years, I had been angry at my brother for not teaching me how to deal with my emotions in a healthy way. But now, as I looked at him, I saw the pain that he carried with him, and I knew that it wasn't his fault. He had done the best he could with the tools that he had been given.

We sat in silence for a few moments, both lost in our own thoughts. Then, my brother spoke up.

"I know that I can't change the past," he said. "But I want to do better in the future. I want to be there for you and the rest of the family. I want to be the kind of person that you can rely on, not just someone who uses violence to solve his problems."

I smiled at my brother, feeling a glimmer of hope. "I know you can do it," I said. "And I'll be here to support you every step of the way."

My brother smiled back at me, and for the first time in a long time, I felt a sense of peace between us. We had both been through so much, and we had both made mistakes. But in that moment, it felt like we were both moving forward, determined to do better and be better.

As we hugged each other tightly, I felt a sense of gratitude wash over me. I was grateful for my brother, for all that he had done for me, even when he didn't know.

I often find myself wondering if people really know me at all. They see me as emotionless, detached, and cold. But that couldn't be further from the truth. Just because I don't wear my heart on my sleeve, doesn't mean I don't feel things deeply.

In fact, I've learned to cope with my misery and detach from my conditioned emotional responses. It's a survival mechanism that I developed early on in life. Growing up with a drug addict for a mother and a brother who had to become my father at the age of 10, I had to learn how to fend for myself. And part of that meant learning how to deal with the pain and suffering that came with that kind of life.

But just because I've learned how to cope, doesn't mean I'm immune to the negative effects of it all. I still feel the weight of the past, the 'woulda, coulda, shoulda's' that bring about personal agony to my present.

It's not that I dwell on the past, but sometimes it feels like the past won't let go of me. I think about all the things I could have done differently, all the mistakes I made, and it's like a weight on my shoulders that I can't shake off.

I try not to let it show, but sometimes it's hard to hide. I'll be sitting in a meeting, or having a conversation with a friend, and suddenly I'll feel the weight of the past bearing down on me. My mind will drift to memories I'd rather forget, and I'll feel a wave of emotion rising up inside of me.

It's in those moments that I feel the most alone. I know I have people in my life who care about me, but it's hard to let them in. It's hard to show them the vulnerable side of me that I try so hard to keep hidden.

But I also know that I can't keep it bottled up forever. Sooner or later, it's going to come out. I'm going to have to face the past and all the pain that comes with it.

It's a scary thought, but it's also liberating. Because I know that once I face it, I can finally start to let it go. I can start to move forward and create a better future for myself.

So I take a deep breath and try to focus on the present moment. I remind myself that the past is just that, the past. It doesn't define me, and it doesn't have to dictate my future.

And slowly but surely, I start to feel the weight lifting off my shoulders. It's not gone completely, but it's lighter than it was before.

I know it won't be easy, but I'm ready to face the past head on. I'm ready to let go of the 'woulda, coulda, shoulda's' and start living in the present.

Because even though the past may have shaped me, it doesn't have to define me. I can still create a future that's better than anything I ever thought possible. And that's something to be excited about.

When I think about my journey and all that I've accomplished, I go to the thought of what started me on that path of 'doing the right thing.' My mission (once I came home from juvenile) was to be a proper example for you and Sweety, so that y'all would know that anything is possible, especially if I could do it! So even though I was still in the streets hustling, I had a plan, and I stuck to it. My first goal was getting back in school after being permanently kicked out for two years. Next, I had to be disciplined enough to stay in school despite the fact that I couldn't read, write, or spell. Once I achieved the first two goals, I set my sights on graduating, which I thought was impossible, but I didn't let that hinder me from pursuing it. When it was all said and done, I accomplished what I set out to accomplish, which, in turn, allowed for you and Sweety to have an established guideline to follow. Also, me going to college is part of that as well.

I remember the visits to see my brother in prison like they were yesterday. The sterile environment, the constant surveillance, the way every conversation was recorded and scrutinized. It was a harsh reminder of the reality of his situation. But despite all of that, we managed to find a way to make the best of it.

One of the ways we passed the time was by coming up with movie scripts and stories. We would sit in the visiting room, the only place we could have a semblance of privacy, and just start talking. At first, it was just a way to fill the silence and distract ourselves from the bleakness of the situation. But soon, it became so much more.

We would start by brainstorming ideas, throwing out plot points and characters and settings. And then we would build on them, adding details and twists and turns. It was like a collaborative art project, with each of us adding our own unique touch to the story.

I remember one script we came up with in particular. It was a gritty crime drama, set in the seedy underbelly of our hometown. We spent hours discussing the plot, the characters, the setting. We debated the finer points of the dialogue, tweaking it until it was just right. We even came up with a killer soundtrack to go along with the movie.

As we wrote, I could see the glint in my brother's eyes. It was like he was transported to another world, one where he wasn't stuck behind bars, but was free to create and explore and dream. And I was happy to be the one to take him there.

It wasn't just a distraction, though. Writing those scripts became a way for us to process our emotions, to work through the pain and frustration and anger that we both felt. It was cathartic, in a way, to pour all of those emotions into something creative, something that could be shared with others.

And it wasn't just about us, either. We knew that the other inmates were listening in on our conversations, and we wanted to give them something to look forward to. We wanted to show them that even in the darkest of places, there was still room for creativity and hope.

Of course, we never actually made any of those movies. We never had the resources or the connections to turn our ideas into reality. But that didn't matter. The act of creation was enough. It was something that no one could take away from us, something that we could hold onto even after the visits were over and we had to go our separate ways.

Looking back on those visits now, I realize just how important they were to both of us. They were a lifeline, a way to stay connected even when the world seemed to be pulling us apart. They were a reminder that even in the darkest of times, there is still room for laughter and creativity and love.

And that movie script, the one we spent so many hours writing? It may never see the light of day, but it will always hold a special place in my heart. It was a testament to the power of the human spirit, to our ability to find hope and beauty even in the most dire of circumstances.

I don't know what the future holds, for me or for my brother. But I do know that those visits, and those movie scripts, will always be a part of our story. They will always be a reminder of the bond that we share, and the strength that we have together.

Here's one of my favorites:

A Father's Spirit

It's <u>Sunday morning</u> and John is getting ready for church. He takes a shower and brushes his teeth while his wife Mary is in the kitchen cooking breakfast (a camera shot of the kitchen).

After cleaning himself up, John puts on his best suit and sits on his bed, grabbing his wedding photo off the nightstand (flashbacks of memories of his wedding night). Mary calls out to John that breakfast is ready, and he snaps out of his daydream (camera now focuses on the kitchen).

Mary fixes John a plate as he enters the kitchen, greeting him with "morning love," but John doesn't respond, which is not unusual for him. He grabs his plate and starts to eat. After two bites, Mary asks,

"How is it?" John's response is shocking to Mary: "It's horrible. You can't do anything right. I can't believe I made you my wife."

Mary is shocked by what she just heard and angrily asks, " What did you say!?" John takes a moment before he replies. After about 10 seconds, John goes into a rant about how he feels like he wasted his youth with a woman who is unable to bear a child and unwilling to consider adoption. Mary stares at John as she holds back tears. The couple's argument escalates, and John storms out of the house, leaving Mary alone. As Mary tries to compose herself, she hears a loud noise upstairs. Thinking it's John, she goes to investigate, only to find that he's not there. Suddenly, the house goes quiet. Mary calls out to John, but there's no answer. As she heads back downstairs, she hears a strange sound coming from the kitchen. When she turns the corner, she sees a shadowy figure standing in front of her. She screams and tries to run, but the figure grabs her and pulls her into the darkness.

Later, john stares at his wife's dead body on the floor. He can't believe what he's done. Blood drips from his fingers as he stares in horror at Mary's lifeless eyes, still open as if in shock. A single tear falls from his eyes.

Years Later

It was a beautiful early summer Sunday day, and Jane was excited to start her new life with her two daughters in their new home. She had just gone through an intense divorce with her children's father and was hoping that moving back to her small hometown in Michigan would be the fresh start she needed. Jane's realtor friend showed her the former home of John and Marry Stevens, and Jane immediately fell in love with the house. The house was stunning, with a large yard, beautiful windows, and plenty of space for her and her daughters. After some negotiations with the seller, Jane was able to get a fair price on the house, and they moved in.

The first few weeks were great, but things took a turn for the worse when strange things began to happen. Jane heard strange noises in the middle of the night, and her daughters complained about feeling cold spots in certain areas of the house. Jane tried to brush it off, thinking it was just their imagination or the house settling, but things only got worse.

One night, as Jane was putting her daughters to bed, they heard a faint voice.

Voice: "Daddy, can you read me a bedtime story?"

Jane was spooked, but she tried to reassure her daughters that it was probably just the house settling.

But as the days went on, the strange occurrences continued. Jane decided to do some research on the history of the house and discovered the tragic story of John and Marry Stevens. She couldn't believe that such a horrible thing had happened in her new home. The more she learned about the story, the more she began to realize that the strange occurrences might be connected to the tragic events that took place in the house.

One night, as Jane was lying in bed, she heard a faint voice.

Voice: "I just want to be a father."

Jane was frightened but decided to investigate. She began to feel a presence in the house, and she knew that it was the spirit of John Stevens. She tried to communicate with the spirit, hoping to find out what it wanted.

Jane: "John, what do you want?"

John: "I just want to be a father. I was so desperate to have children, and when I couldn't, I lost control. But now, I'm trapped here, and I can't move on."

Jane knew that she had to help John find peace so that her family could live in the house without fear. She contacted a local spiritualist who was able to help John's spirit find peace. With the spiritualist's help, John's spirit was finally able to move on, and Jane and her daughters could finally live in their new home without fear.

Elizabeth: "Mom, what was that man?" Jane: "Just a man who got lost."

Laura: "Did he go to heaven?"

Jane: "I hope so."

I had to watch my brother show strength by being under the control of the state and listen to men I know he would break in half. So my job became even more tough so I had to help him escape his current reality and give him hope. So we wrote a movie script just by sitting their in the visiting room. I know my brother will always be strong but to watch your hero have to take a step back because he know correctional officers have power struggles was hard to watch. So message to my brother your body is locked up don't let them lock your mind keep being creative and I'll write a million movies with you just to help you escape them 4 walls even when it's for a minute.

Chapter 7:
I'm Fighting For My Life

Watching my mom struggle with severe drug addiction, being a crack baby, and being one of seven siblings who have been to jail or prison, has been one of the most draining things for me. Since I was the last child of my mom, I felt that I had to change the dynamics of the reputation of my siblings and our last name. All of my siblings have been charged with a crime or two before, including murder, armed robbery, drug-related offenses, and theft. Statistically, I am not supposed to have a master's degree; I am supposed to be either in jail or dead. I fight for my life every day because I didn't have a sibling role model to show me the way to success; they only taught me how to survive on the EASTSIDE of Detroit. Now, I am trying to unlearn the ways of convicted felons around me and hold us up to a higher standard.

I hear all the whispers saying, "Oh, how all Shell's kids are smart, but they won't be anything because their mom is a crackhead." People have given my siblings every opportunity to feel as if that is true. Now, I realize that I am giving people too much credit. If my mom was the black sheep of the family, what makes me think her children are not as well? What if they prayed for us to not be worth it because they saw how special mom could have been? What if everybody saw how special Mama was, but she couldn't see it because of the anger from her childhood? I got us, Ma. I made sure that I earned a bachelor's and master's degree and never went to jail. I am also sorry for everything you have been through as a child. I wish I could have fought for you. You know I wouldn't let anything happen to you. I am sorry that you were beaten for being left-handed and that you were raped in foster care. I understand why "Shell" exists because anyone who went through what you went through would have turned to something negative to take away their pain. I know, Mom, you just want to feel good. I am glad you don't have to suffer anymore. I used to always hear you say you were tired, but you stayed around for your children. You are gangsta for that. That's what the love of a parent looks like. You endured pain no human should endure, yet you still stand tall, beautiful, with a head full of hair, and your head held high. You don't look like what you have been through at all.

You taught me how to fight for my life because if you didn't fight for yours, I wouldn't be here today. How can any of your children hate you when you gave us the tools needed to keep pushing no matter what the situation is? You gave us hope, a strong mind, thick skin, determination, fearlessness, and taught us not to care about what people think because they are going through what you are going through; they are just ashamed of their story. You taught us how to stand tall and not depend on anybody to fight our battles. Even in loss, you taught us to take things with a grain of salt and always be a light for somebody else because everybody is not as strong as you, and they may need you to help them.

Even when we were on government assistance and section 8, you let people come live with us, and we barely had a place in a three-bedroom house to sleep. But you understood how it felt to be outside in the cold in the winter, so you opened your house to anyone who needed a place to stay. You experienced life in the cold, going from shelter to shelter, and even family members turning their backs on you.

You moved from the west to the east to get away from everybody. Thank God you made me an EASTSIDER; I'll always love you for that, lol.

On a serious note, I never had to fight for my life because you already prepared me to fight for it, so essentially you already fought for me and trained me to fight. I'm just getting in a finished ring to go to the places you couldn't go to. You started the fight, but I'm going to finish it. The love I thought you didn't have for me was there this whole time; you just taught us real love to prepare us for the hard situations that people like us have to endure. People don't always say "I love you," but they show it by preparing you for things life can't prepare you for unless they had the mom we had who had been through it. Your experience built us for moments like this when our stove goes out, we can make a meal in the microwave. When the lights go off, we get creative and play games in the dark, like walking tag. I ran into the basement pole so many times playing walking tag when the lights were out; great times.

What I'm trying to say, Mom, is that I want to say sorry for everybody who hurt you and never told you sorry because you deserve to hear sorry. So if they never told you, I'm sorry. Allow it to come from your child. Mom, I'm sorry, and I'm not angry at them for hurting you because they made you who you needed to be so that your children can be exactly who we needed to be.

Chapter 8:
Learning Life My Way
(Therapy Time)

They always say a man is not supposed to cry, but damn, how much am I supposed to take before it's okay to drop a tear? I think it's time to go to therapy.

"What brings you in today?" the therapist asked.

"To be honest, I don't know. In order for me to help you, you have to be open, or you'll be paying me for nothing. Now, if you want your money to go to waste, you can keep blocking out what you hear, or you can tell me so we can work through it together."

"I hated my mom for so long, and I know deep in my head I shouldn't, and I'm tired of hating her."

"Why do you hate your mom? Tell me why?" the therapist asked.

"I feel like she put drugs over her own fucking kids, like we don't fucking matter."

"It's okay to be angry, but why do you think she put drugs over y'all?"

"Food stamps getting sold, lights, gas, and water getting turned off, and she leaves for days at a time."

"Why is she on drugs?"

"Do it fucking matter? She has kids now to look after. I would never do my kids like she did us." As I end the session abruptly and walk out.

"Dang it, I failed myself again. I tried to go get help and wasn't ready to face the reality that I'm contributing to my own failure, and I couldn't keep blaming my childhood or my mom. Now I have to look myself in the mirror and become the man that I want to be on my own. Everybody and everything can't keep taking responsibility for myself. It took me 2 years to go back to therapy and get some help. The process of me getting back into therapy changed my life for the better, and I took off and never looked back."

"How are you doing?" the therapist asked on my first day back in therapy.

"Since this is a safe place, I'm not okay. I still have a lot of things to work through, and I want to be healed and not be so angry."

"It's a lot of trauma that you have to work through, and you can't rush your healing process. You have to take it one day at a time."

"These days are becoming long as shit. Why can't she just say sorry so I can fucking move on with my life?"

"Have you tried to talk to her and tell her your side of the true story?"

"Man fuck yeah, she doesn't want to hear that shit. She just wants to block it out like it never happened. And when I try to get her to really hear my side, she just says, 'Y'all not going to give me no guilt trip. That's y'all life. Y'all grown now.' So since I can't punch her, I punched other people. She's the reason why I used to snap on people because I could never hit her. So I hit other people. Fuck 'em."

"I encourage you to pace yourself and be okay with being uncomfortable with this process of healing. Let's do an exercise if you don't mind."

"What is it?"

"I'm going to sit right here in front of you, and you're going to act like I'm your mom, and you're going to say everything that you would want to say to her to me."

"I don't think this is going to work, and I really don't want to do this." "If you feel like it's not working, we can always stop."

"Okay, let's do it."

"Baby, I hear you wanted to talk to me about something."

Tears instantly started to slide down my face, and all the anger I felt as a child when I saw a man serving her drugs came back, and I could have punched my therapist clean in the face for bringing back all of those memories and feelings that I worked 15 years to bury back to the surface. 'Fuck man, I can't do this.' 'It's okay. I'm here with you. Let's go slow. Just tell your mom one thing at a time.' As I wiped my face, I started to get back into character. 'Okay, mom.' I dropped my head because I couldn't find the words. It was like she walked in the room and was listening to me. I wanted to speak, but I couldn't. As my therapist gave me a hug, it gave me courage. 'Why the fuck do you have to use crack? Why can't you be a normal mom and just love me? I'm dying without you every fucking day, and you just don't give a fuck.' My therapist was shocked but instantly remembered he had to get back into character. 'Me using drugs isn't your fault.' I cut her off immediately. 'But it's affecting me the most. You only came to one of my football games, and if you didn't fucking know, mom, I'm pretty damn good,' I raged. 'I'm so proud of you, baby. I always knew you would be good at everything you do.' It's like my therapist knew my mom personally and knew how she used to soften us up whenever we wanted to confront her. 'Mom, that's not the point. I just need you more than you need drugs. Why can't I be your drug? Why aren't we enough?' 'You all are enough. You all are my most prized possession. I use fewer drugs because of y'all. I'm an addict because of what I went through in my past.' 'Mom, you know it's embarrassing to call my coach to go spend the night at his house because you're too high, and I hate seeing you like this.' 'I'm sorry, baby, but I hate seeing me like this too, and I'm glad you have somebody to be an outlet. I had nobody to be what your coaches are for you."

Chapter 9:
Built to Last

The cards have always been stacked against me, but I have always found a way to go from the bottom to the top. Born addicted to crack, I still was born a healthy size because, no matter what, I'm built to last. Most babies yearn for milk, while I was yearning for my next high, my next dose of poison. "Why is he shaking? What's wrong with my baby?" Momma asked. The doctor replied with a somber look, "Ma'am, the drugs must wear off. He's going through withdrawals." While I was able to go home within the first 3 months, I never knew the danger I'd face under my mother's care. My withdrawal symptoms were not limited to the shakes; I cried profusely. No matter how many diaper changes, lullabies, or milk I was given, nothing relaxed me because none of those things gave me the feeling of the drugs that I had been subjected to during the entire pregnancy, so for the first 3 months of my life, I withdrew from being a crack baby.

Momma knows best, though. Or does she? Imagine having a cap full of liquor diluted in your formula and inhaling the smoke purposely blown in your face to "help you calm down" or quiet the fussy baby. It's only so much you can take, for God's sake. I'm only three months old. I hate that I went looking for this information because just when I thought I was over the hurt she caused, it's like she purposely does something that makes me question why me and why was I born unto her. I didn't deserve to be loved, cuddled, and secured like a regular baby. Why didn't you love me enough to abort me instead of bringing me into a world of pain? Can you imagine your mother ignoring your cries because she's tired of you having the shakes? I didn't cause me to have an early childhood addiction. Mom, why can't you just love me? I don't need or want anything in this world except your love. None of the things in this world that I accomplish matters because your love has always felt so absent. I will give back both of my degrees just to feel the full effect of your love when you are not under the influence of drugs or alcohol for one day. Sadly, you are not here with me, and I know you were tired of the pain that you were suffering in this world, so I want you to know I forgive you for every age of my life. From day one until now, thanks for teaching me how to survive in a world of toxic individuals, but, Mom, I learned how to love on my own and I found love. I know you would have liked her; she's wild just like you, with no filter, wears a lot of wigs, and sleeps all day, just like you. Lol, it's like I fell in love with exactly who you were.

To my mother, I was a nuisance. My birth was never planned, nor was I created out of love. Somehow, I was the accident from two individuals trading favors. Strung out and lacking the parental abilities to raise us, we were sent off as unsolicited gifts to various family members. Unfortunately, I was the black sheep nobody wanted. Not because of anything I did, but because nobody wanted the crackhead cry baby suffering from withdrawals. From day one, I could've counted myself out like everyone else did, but no, not me. I use these experiences as stepping stones to build a better future for me and my family. Everything they said I couldn't do or wouldn't do, I made it my obligation to shut the naysayers down!

I'm worthy as long as I have breath in my body. I went from being a crack baby to someone that nobody wanted to winning MVP trophies in football and becoming really good at it. I heard one of my basketball coaches say, "Where is his mother? I have never seen her at a game, a parent-teacher conference, or anything," and laughed as if he had told a funny joke. Well, the joke's on you. I was better at basketball than your son, and I am more successful today. Maybe you shouldn't have gone to his games and abandoned him. Maybe, just maybe, he might have been good.

Chapter 10:
Life Lessons From the Past

Life was tough growing up, as we didn't have a lot of money, and my mom's addiction meant that we didn't always have a stable home life. My mom would often be shell for days on end, leaving me to fend for myself. I had to grow up quickly and learn how to take care of myself.

As a child, I didn't fully understand my mom's addiction and the impact it had on our lives. I just knew that things were different in our household compared to my friends' homes. I felt embarrassed and ashamed of my situation, and I didn't want anyone to know about it. I tried to hide it the best I could, but it was challenging.

As I got older, I started to realize the extent of my mom's addiction and how it had affected me. I had to deal with a lot of emotions that I didn't know how to handle, and I didn't have anyone to turn to for support. I felt angry, sad, and frustrated all at once. I didn't know how to cope, and so I turned to other things to help me numb the pain.

When I was just a teenager, I started experimenting with women and sex. I didn't want to be like my mom, but I also didn't know how to deal with my emotions. I felt like I had no control over my life, and sex and flings were the only things that made me feel better.

As I got older, I continued to struggle with relationships, particularly with women. I didn't trust easily, and I was always worried that they would leave me, just like my mom had. So, I left them first. I didn't consider their feelings and only thought about myself no matter what.

I didn't understand why I was like this, but I knew that it was a problem. I would try to control my behavior, but I couldn't help the way I felt. I would constantly push women away, even if I cared a little about them, because I was afraid of getting hurt. I realize now that this was a way of protecting myself.

It wasn't until I sought out therapy that I started to understand why I was struggling so much with relationships. My therapist helped me to see that my mom's addiction had left me with a lot of emotional baggage, and that I needed to work through it in order to move forward.

Through therapy, I learned how to cope with my emotions in a healthy way. I started to understand why I was feeling the way I was, and I learned how to communicate my feelings to others. I also worked on building trust with the women in my life, which helped me to form healthier relationships.

I still have moments where I struggle, but I now have the tools to deal with my emotions in a healthy way. I'm grateful that I sought out help and that I'm now able to form healthy relationships with the women in my life. It's been a long and difficult journey, but I feel like I've come a long way.

Growing up with my drug-addicted mom was tough enough, but her views on love and relationships made it even harder for me. She believed that love was not real and that it only led to pain and disappointment. She taught me and my siblings that we should never rely on anyone else and that we should always put ourselves first.

This mentality affected me in all of my relationships with women. I didn't believe in love, and I thought that getting attached to someone would only lead to heartache. I was never in a real relationship; I only had casual sex with women and then quickly pushed them away. I thought that this was the best way to protect myself from getting hurt.

But the reality was that I was hurting myself even more. I felt empty and alone, and I didn't know how to form a genuine connection with someone. I would use sex as a way to feel better temporarily, but it never fulfilled me.

It wasn't until I met someone who was different that my perspective began to shift. As you know, her name was Tyesha, and she was a kind, compassionate woman who saw the best in everyone. We met through mutual friends, and I was immediately drawn to her. We started spending more time together, and I began to open up to her in ways that I never had before.

At first, I was afraid of getting too close to her. I didn't want to let my guard down and risk getting hurt. But she was patient with me, and she showed me that love could be real and that it didn't have to be painful.

As our relationship grew, I realized that I had been missing out on something important. I had been so focused on protecting myself that I had never allowed myself to experience the beauty of love. Tyesha showed me that love was not just about physical attraction, but it was also about emotional connection and mutual respect.

But even with Tyesha, I still struggled with my insecurities and fears. I was afraid of losing her, and I found myself becoming jealous and possessive. I didn't want to lose the one person who had shown me what real love was, but my behavior was pushing her away.

It wasn't until I sought out therapy that I started to understand the root of my issues. My therapist helped me to see that my mom's views on love had affected me deeply and that I needed to work through my fears in order to form healthy relationships.

Through therapy, I learned how to communicate my feelings to Tyesha in a healthy way. I started to understand that my jealousy and possessiveness were rooted in my own insecurities, and that it was not her fault. I worked on building trust with her and learning how to be vulnerable in a relationship.

Tyesha and I have been together for three years now, and I can honestly say that she has changed my life for the better. She has taught me that love can be real and that it can bring immense joy and fulfillment to our lives. I'm grateful for her patience, kindness, and unwavering love, and I'm excited to continue growing and learning with her by my side.

Before her, my relationships were shallow and unfulfilling. I never allowed myself to get close to anyone, and I used physical intimacy as a way to feel better temporarily. I didn't want to risk getting hurt, so I would push women away as soon as they started to show any sign of attachment.

I had a string of <u>one-night</u> stands and short-term flings, but they never brought me any real happiness. I felt empty and alone, even when I was with someone else.

My fear of getting close to anyone had begun when I was a child. My mom's drug addiction had caused her to be absent and unreliable, leaving me and my siblings to fend for ourselves. I had learned from a young age that I couldn't rely on anyone else, and that it was safer to keep people at arm's length.

This fear had translated into my adult life, making it impossible for me to form healthy relationships. I would have sex with women but would never allow myself to get emotionally involved. I liked the physical aspect of it, but I didn't want to deal with the emotional baggage that came with it.

As a result, my relationships never lasted long. Women would become frustrated with my behavior and would eventually give up on me. I knew that I was hurting them, but I didn't know how to change. To be honest, I didn't even really care enough to. As I mentioned before, these women never really mattered to me.

I would even go so far as to throw them out of my house if they tried to spend the night. I didn't like the idea of someone else being in my space, and I certainly didn't want anyone to see me vulnerable in the morning. Some women would try and cuddle after sex and I'd immediately turn them down. I didn't want no one touching me unless it was on my own terms.

Looking back on it now, I realize how much damage I was doing to myself and to others. My fear of getting close to anyone was only hurting me in the end. I was left feeling empty and alone, with no real connection to anyone.

It wasn't until I met Tyesha that I began to understand the damage I had been doing to myself. She showed me that emotional connection was just as important as physical intimacy, and that true happiness could only come from forming genuine relationships.

But before her, my fear of getting close to anyone had consumed me, leaving me unable to form healthy relationships.

As I look back on my past relationships, I am filled with regret and shame. I realize now that my behavior was a defense mechanism, a way to protect myself from getting hurt. But in doing so, I hurt those around me and caused damage that can never be undone.

I treated women as objects, using them for physical pleasure and then discarding them when I was done. I never allowed myself to get close to anyone, always keeping them at arm's length. I was so afraid of getting hurt that I didn't even consider the feelings of those around me.

It wasn't until much later that I realized how much damage I had caused. I saw the hurt and pain in the eyes of the women I had been with, and I knew that I had been the cause of it. I had used them and then thrown them away, never caring about the consequences of my actions.

Looking back, I realize that my behavior was a coping mechanism, a way to deal with the pain of my childhood. My mom's drug addiction had left me with a deep sense of abandonment and mistrust, and I had carried those wounds with me into adulthood. I had never learned how to form healthy relationships, and I had used physical intimacy as a way to fill the void.

But now, as I look back, I realize how wrong I was. I see the damage that I caused, and I am filled with regret. I wish that I could go back in time and treat those women with the respect and kindness that they deserved. I wish that I had been able to form genuine connections and to open myself up to the possibility of love.

But it's too late for that now. The damage has been done, and all I can do is try to make amends. I can try to be a better person, to learn from my mistakes and to never repeat them again.

In therapy, I am learning how to form healthy relationships and how to trust others. It's a long and difficult process, but I am committed to it. I know that I can never undo the damage that I caused, but I can try to make things right going forward.

Looking back on my past relationships is painful, but it's also a reminder of how far I have come. I am no longer the person that I used to be, and I am committed to being a better person in the future.

As I reflect on my past, I can't help but think about the kind of father I want to be. I know that I have made mistakes, but I also know that I can learn from them and be a better parent.

It wasn't until I had daughters, that want to treat women with love and respect. I want to show them that they are valued and that their feelings matter. I want to be there for them, to support them through the ups and downs of life, and to be a positive influence in their life.

I also know my sons will benefit off the new man I am because I know how to be patient. I want to raise them to be a better men than I was.I want to teach them about the importance of treating women with respect and kindness, and to show them that strength comes from empathy and compassion, not from dominance and control.

I know that being a parent is not easy, and that I will make mistakes along the way. But I also know that I can learn from those mistakes and become a better parent and a better person as a result.

I want to break the cycle of dysfunction that was present in my family and create a new legacy for my own children. I want them to grow up in a home filled with love, respect, and kindness, and to have the tools they need to form healthy relationships with others.

In order to do this, I need to continue to work on myself, to heal the wounds of my past, and to become the best version of myself that I can be. It won't be easy, but I know that it's worth it.

Looking back on my past relationships has been painful, but it has also been a wake-up call. It has shown me the kind of person I don't want to be, and the kind of person I want to become. And if I ever have children, I will do everything in my power to be the kind of parent they deserve.

Chapter 11:
Moving Forward

From a very young age, I realized that life was not going to be easy for me. My mother was addicted to drugs and was not able to provide me with the love and care that every child deserves. As a result, I had to rely on myself to survive. The first few months of my life were especially tough as I had to go through painful withdrawal symptoms. The shakes and the crying seemed to never end, and there was nothing that anyone could do to make it better.

As I grew older, my mother's addiction only got worse. She would withdraw or days on end, leaving me alone and hungry. I learned how to fend for myself, how to find food and shelter when I needed it. It wasn't easy, but I knew that I had to keep going if I wanted to survive.

Despite the odds, I was determined to make something of myself. I had always been a fighter, and I refused to let my circumstances define me. I worked hard in school and was able to excel in my studies. I knew that education was my ticket out of the poverty and despair that I had grown up in.

As I got older, I started to see the world in a different way. I realized that there were people out there who had never experienced the kind of hardship that I had gone through. They had been born into wealth and privilege and had never had to fight for anything. I knew that I could never be like them, but I also knew that I could use my experiences to help others who were struggling.

Over time, I was able to build a new life for myself. I went to college and earned a degree, using my experiences to help others who were struggling. I met someone who loved me for who I was, and we became a family of our own. It was not always easy, but I knew that I was building a better life for myself and my loved ones.

Looking back on my life, I can see that the cards were indeed stacked against me. I was born addicted to drugs, and my mother was unable to care for me. But I also see that I was given something else - a fighting spirit that allowed me to overcome the odds and build a life that I could be proud of.

I know that there are still many challenges ahead, but I am ready for them. I have faced so much already, and I know that I can handle whatever life throws my way. I am grateful for the lessons that I have learned, and I am determined to use my experiences to help others who are struggling.

In the end, I know that it is not about the cards that we are dealt, but about how we play the hand that we are given. I have played mine to the best of my ability, and I am proud of the life that I have built.

The feeling of abandonment and neglect can be overwhelming, especially when it comes from the one person who is supposed to love and protect you unconditionally: your mother. It's hard to fathom the pain and confusion a baby might feel when they are exposed to drugs or alcohol through their mother's breast milk or formula. It's even more heartbreaking when they are deliberately blown smoke in their face to "calm them down." As a child, it's difficult to understand why your own mother would choose to inflict such harm on you. You feel helpless, alone, and unloved, questioning why you were even brought into this world.

It's not just the physical harm that hurts, it's the emotional scars that last a lifetime. As a child, you crave your mother's love and attention, but instead, you are met with indifference, neglect, and abuse. You long for the warmth of her embrace, the comfort of her voice, and the security of her love. But instead, you are left feeling like a burden, an inconvenience, and a disappointment. It's hard not to feel like you are unworthy of love when the one person who is supposed to love you the most treats you like you don't matter.

As you grow older, the pain doesn't go away. It lingers in the back of your mind, haunting you like a ghost from the past. You try to move on, to build a life for yourself, but the wounds never fully heal. You may find success in your career, your relationships, or your personal goals, but it never feels like enough. You still crave your mother's love, even though you know deep down that it may never come.

But despite all of the pain and hurt, there is still room for forgiveness. Forgiveness for your mother's mistakes, for her addictions, and for her shortcomings as a parent. It's not easy, but it's necessary for your own healing. Forgiveness doesn't mean forgetting, and it doesn't mean excusing the behavior. It simply means letting go of the anger and resentment and finding a way to move forward. It's a long and difficult journey, but with time, patience, and love, it is possible.

Growing up with a mother who didn't want me was a challenging experience. It left me feeling rejected, unloved, and unwanted. It's hard to imagine how a mother could view her own child as a nuisance, but unfortunately, it was my reality. Despite this, I was determined to not let this define me. I wanted to prove to myself and others that I was more than what they thought of me.

It's incredible to see how I have not only survived but also thrived in a world filled with toxic individuals. It took strength and resilience to navigate through life when the odds were stacked against me. I learned how to love on my own and found someone who I believe my mother would have liked. It's amazing to see how life has come full circle, and I found someone who reminds me of the mother I love so much.

It's sad to hear that I was considered an accident and not created out of love. However, I've used this as motivation to create a better future for myself and my loved ones. I didn't let the circumstances of my birth define me. Instead, I used those experiences as fuel to drive my ambition and create a better life for myself.

Despite the challenges I've faced, it's clear that I have a bright future ahead of me. I've proven that I am resilient, determined, and capable of achieving anything I set my mind to. I've overcome the odds, and that is a testament to my strength and courage. My story serves as a reminder that it's possible to overcome adversity and create a better future.

I am a product of my past, but I refuse to be a prisoner of it. Life has thrown many challenges and hardships my way, but I am determined to overcome them and become something greater.

Despite being born as a crack baby and not being wanted by anyone, I didn't let that hold me back. I used my experiences as stepping stones to build a better future for myself and my family. I proved to the world that I am worthy and capable of achieving anything I set my mind to.

Even though my mother wasn't there for me the way I needed her to be, I learned how to love on my own and found love with someone who shares my wild spirit. I didn't let my past dictate my future. Instead, I embraced my experiences and used them as motivation to become a better person.

I am grateful for the people in my life who supported me along the way. From my teachers who believed in me to my coaches who pushed me to be my best, I owe a debt of gratitude to those who helped me succeed.

At the end of the day, I am proud of who I am and what I have accomplished. I have come a long way from the crack baby that nobody wanted. I am now a successful and confident individual who knows that I am worthy as long as I have breath in my body.

It can be difficult to love someone who has hurt us deeply, especially when that person is our own mother. However, despite the pain and abuse, I have come to understand that my mother did the best she could with the tools she had.

Beneath the addiction and the abuse, I know that my mother was a good person. She was kind, loving, and compassionate when she was sober. Unfortunately, addiction can be a powerful force that can consume even the best of people.

It was not easy growing up with a mother who was addicted to drugs and alcohol. There were times when I felt neglected and unloved, and there were moments when I wished I was never born. But as I grew older, I came to understand that my mother's addiction was not a reflection of who she was as a person.

I know that my mother loved me in her own way, and I choose to focus on the good times we had together. Despite her addiction, she always tried her best to provide for me and give me the love and attention I needed.

Today, I am grateful for the lessons I learned from my mother, even if they were painful. I learned how to be strong, resilient, and compassionate, and I know that I would not be the person I am today without her.

So, despite the abuse and the pain, I choose to love my mother because I know that she was a good person beneath it all. And even though she is no longer with me, her memory lives on, and I will always cherish the good times we had together.

Final Words to My Mother

Hey Mom, I wrote a book. Crazy, right? I know. Who would have ever thought I'd write a book? Now, hear me out. I know you don't like being vulnerable, but in this book, I let the world hear your side of the story and didn't let people keep talking down on you like they normally do. So I gave you a name again. You are not just Shell, the one who uses drugs or a crackhead. You are the most beautiful woman in the world, Michelle Virginia Dorsey. I hope you don't hate me for not publicly loving you as a child, but see, I learned not to be ashamed of who you were because you taught me how to have confidence no matter who was looking. You taught me how to love even in dark places. This is the thing: I was taught to hate you from an early age because people talked so bad about you. I thought that, in order for me to fit in, I had to as well. It didn't help that I didn't know you were my mom until I was around 5 years old, so it was like meeting a stranger. But when I became accustomed to your warm embrace, it was magic. We never talk about the good heart you had; we only talk about the dark days and the dark side of your heart. I understand why you had to turn your emotions and feelings off to survive. You were beaten, raped, put out at 18, unloved, and abandoned. Anyone that walked in your shoes would have never been as kind-hearted as you. Instead of people helping you, they gave up on you, even one of your children. I appreciate having Quan and Martinez as big brothers because they taught me that no matter what, family is family. So they taught me how to love you even when you couldn't love yourself.

Mom, I forgive you. I know you forgive me. I just wish my phone could ring one last time, and it's you on the other end telling me to come pick you up now to get your nails done and give Ryan the money for your ponytail. Oh, before you go, Mom, I got my Masters, and I'm one year away from my Doctorate. I'm saving the Dorsey's last name. You're lit now. We play Anita Baker whenever we think about you, and your daughters haven't stopped crying since you passed. I don't cry because you told us not to. Lol. I wish I could keep you forever, but I know you have to get back to watching over the rest of your kids. They need you more because they still have anger issues. Smh. I'm still your sweet, sweet baby boy. Lol. I love you, Michelle Virginia Dorsey.

About the Author

I am a crack baby that was born with withdraws to a home where all of my siblings are convicted felons and my mom was on drugs. I am the only one of my sibling to not go to jail and to have two degrees and working on a third degree I have a Masters in Psychology and getting my EDD in educational leadership. I had all the pressure on me being my mom last child to try to get a degree with the world falling apart around me. My mom used to leave us in the home alone for days at a time to go get high so we grew an unbreakable bond as siblings because we had to have each other back and take care of each other. My brother Quan became the man of the house at 10 years old not because he wanted to but simply because my mom told him he was the man of the house. He was 5 years older than me so at 10 it lead him to stealing and selling drugs early so that we can have decent clothes for school and some food on the table. I wanted love and didn't feel like I received it until I understood they loved me as much as they knew how. This is why the book is a double entendre because the love they showed prepared me for the tough times growing up on the eastside of Detroit.

Made in the USA
Monee, IL
22 July 2023

39523824R00056